CW00798812

First published in 1996
This paperback edition published 2001

Copyright Steven Appleby © 1996

The moral right of the author
has been asserted.

Bloomsbury Publishing PLC
38 Soho Square, London W1D 3HB

ISBN 0 7475 5860 4

Printed in Italy by
Editoriale Johnson SpA

by
Steven
Appleby

AGE 20

Life is limitless. I'm immortal. Anything is possible...

AGE 25

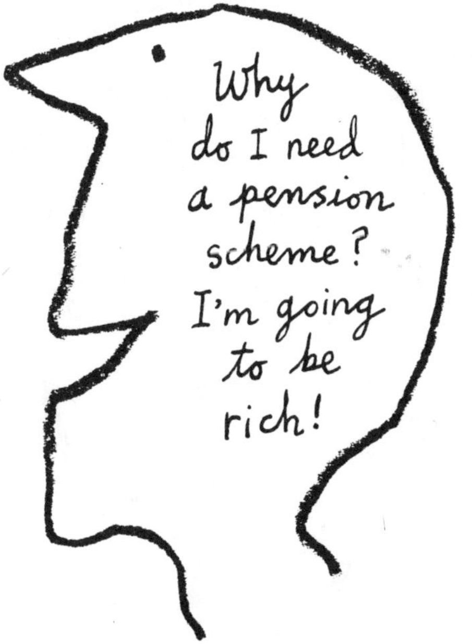

AGE 30

Life's not halfway through... There's still plenty of time... I can do anything...

AGE 40

Life's not going quite according to plan, but bags of time left... Things can still change...

AGE 50

What have I done with my life?! God, it's nearly over! I've achieved nothing!! etc...

I wonder if girls think I'm good-looking...

Oh how dreadful... Poor, poor you...
I'm saying that so you'll think I'm a nice person.

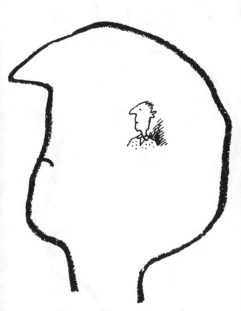

SMALL-MINDED

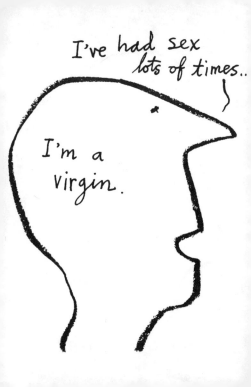

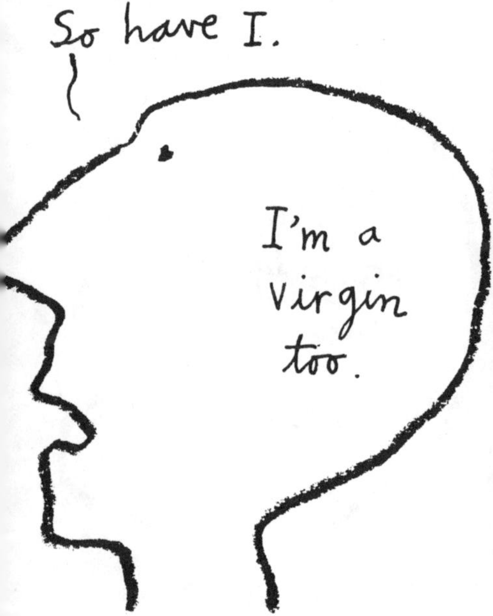
So have I.
I'm a virgin too.

Ho ho... me neither. Ugh!
Except for that time with John. And Stewart... And...

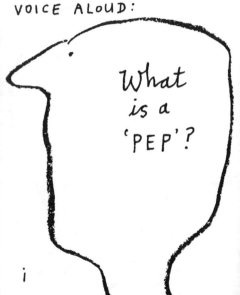

Is it
FA cup
final day?
Which
teams are
playing?

ii

Where, exactly, is the clitoris and what does it look like?

iii

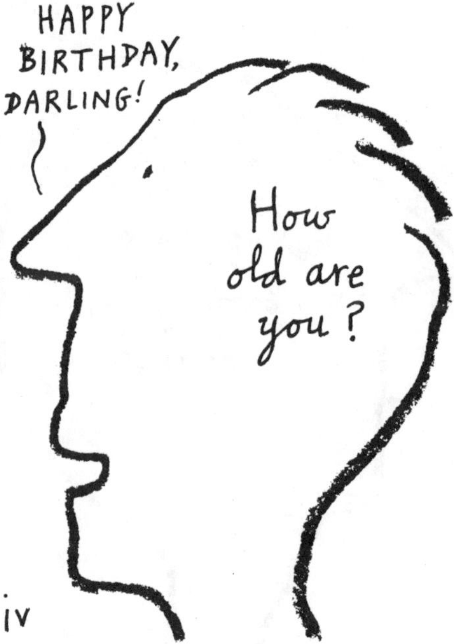
HAPPY BIRTHDAY, DARLING!
How old are you?

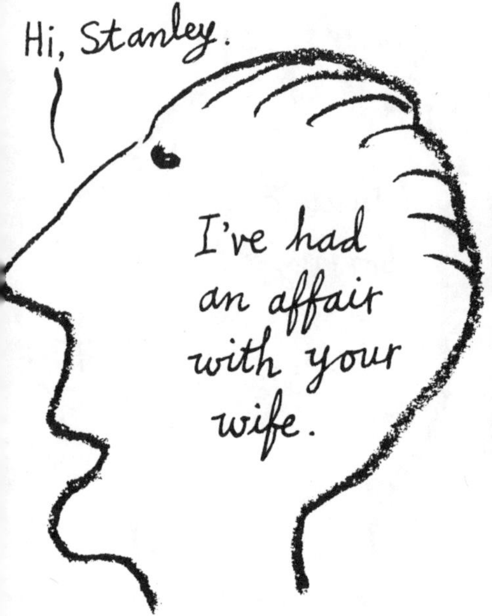
Hi, Stanley.
I've had an affair with your wife.

What a boring person Jim is.

Hello, Jim.

I have a horrible suspicion that I'm a boring person.
Hello, Bob.

I've left
my flies
open
deliberately.

Do you love me?
Yes.
No...
Maybe...
Don't know...
Perhaps...
But I do want to have sex with you.

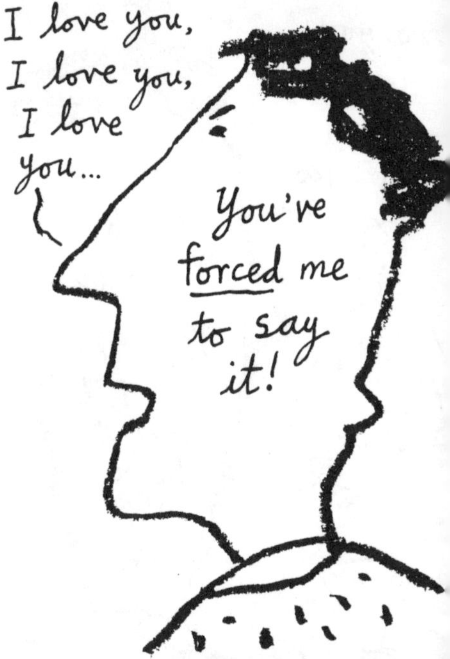
I love you, I love you, I love you...
You've forced me to say it!

Do you
really?
Of
course...
not.
But I
don't
want to
hurt
your
feelings.

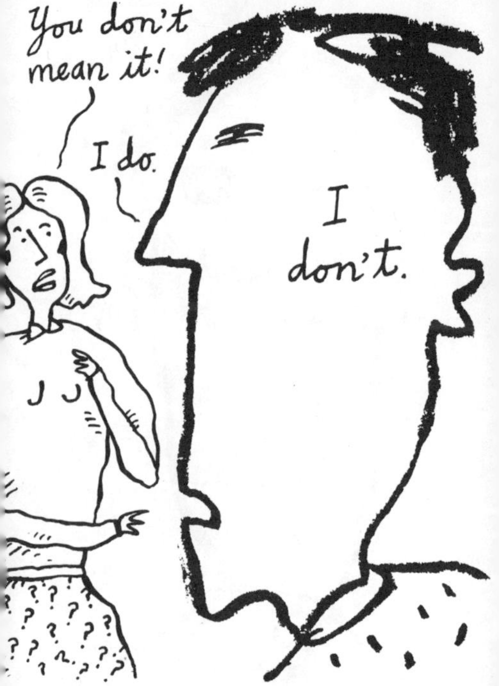
You don't mean it!
I do.
I don't.

my
wife
doesn't know
I'm here
wearing only
a rubber
helmet.

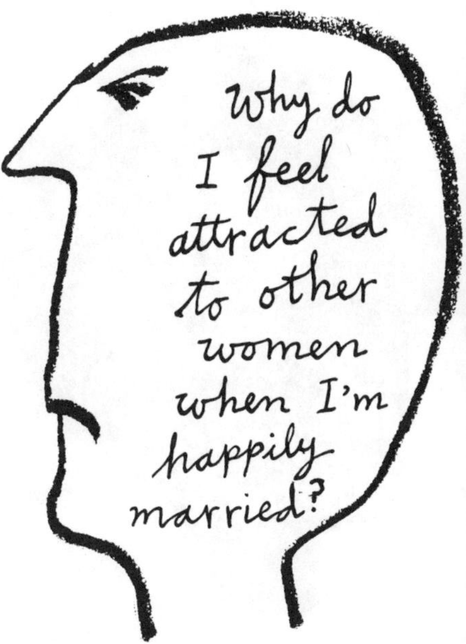
Why do
I feel
attracted
to other
women
when I'm
happily
married?

Can men and women be friends without sex getting in the way?
Yes indeed!

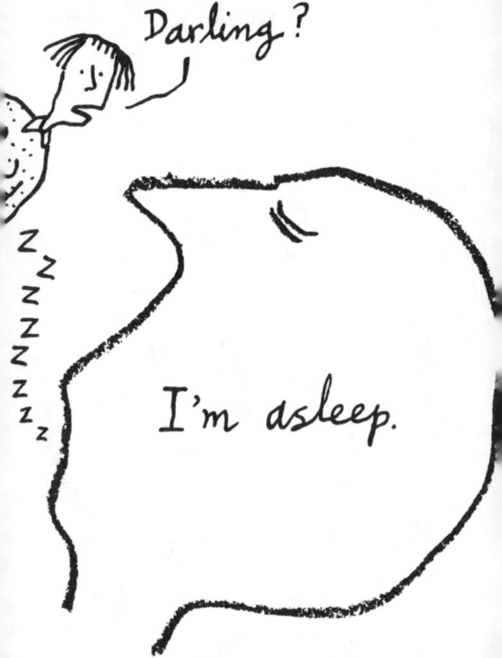
Darling?
ZZZZZZZZZ
I'm asleep.

I
wonder
what it
would
be like
to
murder
someone...

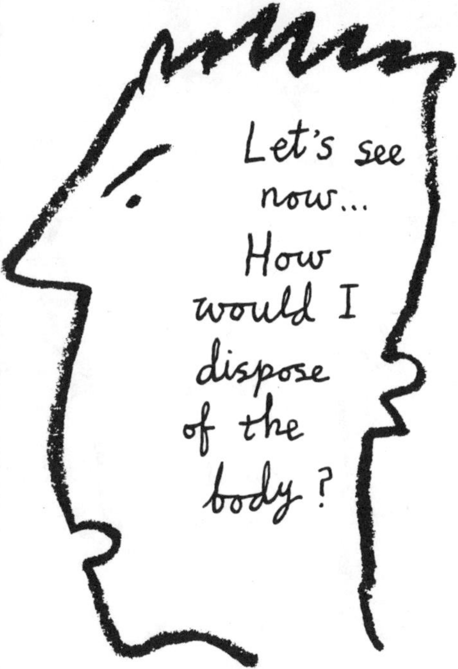
Let's see
now...
How
would I
dispose
of the
body?

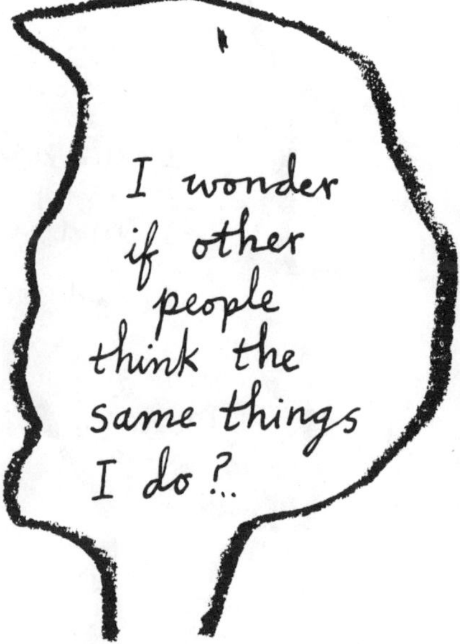
I wonder if other people think the same things I do?..

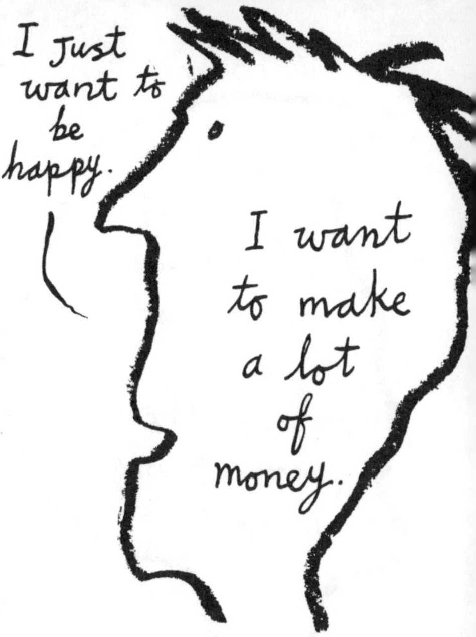
I just want to be happy.
I want to make a lot of money.

The lawnmower and other household items have become indifferent to me.
WN...

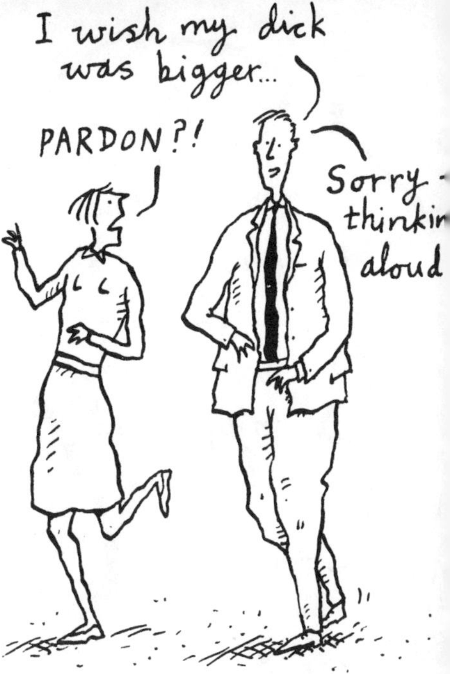
I wish my dick was bigger...
PARDON?!
Sorry - thinkin
aloud

Of course, it's well known that women suffer from penis envy.

They wouldn't envy mine if they knew how small it is.

Meet Roger. He's really sensitive. A new man.
Hi.
You lucky thing, Fiona
Hi, Roger.
God. Look at those tits!

I've put the washing on; I'll do some ironing then start the supper if you like...

Please say no. I want to put my feet up and watch T.V. while you feed me.

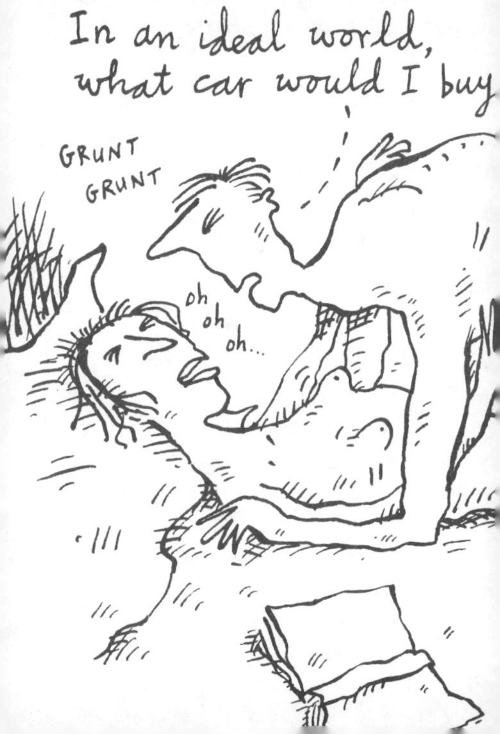
In an ideal world, what car would I buy
GRUNT GRUNT
oh oh oh...

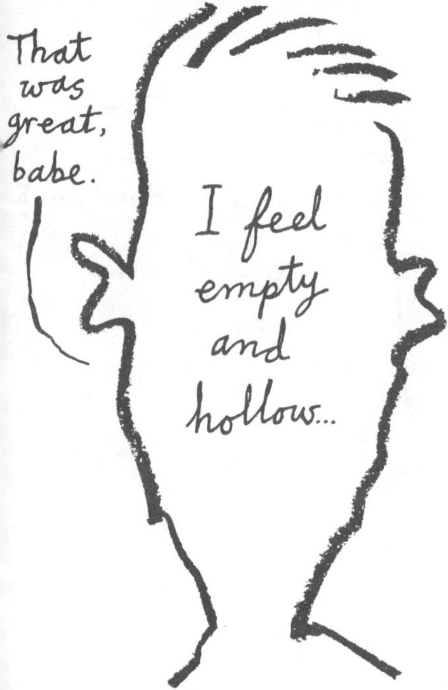
That was great, babe.
I feel empty and hollow...

Neither
do I.

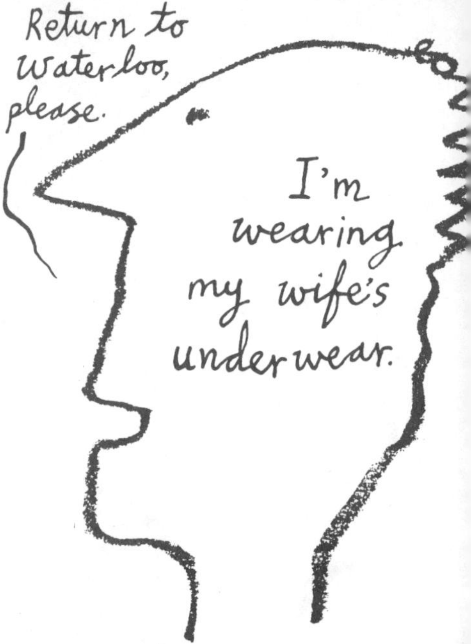
Return to Waterloo, please.
I'm wearing my wife's underwear.

I
hope I
don't get
knocked down
by a car
and need to
have my
clothing
cut
off...

My family are the most important thing in my life.
The children? My wife looks after them.

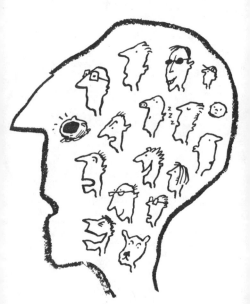

MULTIPLE PERSONALITY

I am a
creature
from
another
planet.

Ruth's a couple of hours late home. I hope she's okay.
Maybe she's been run over and killed. That would get me out of this relationship and solve my money worries.

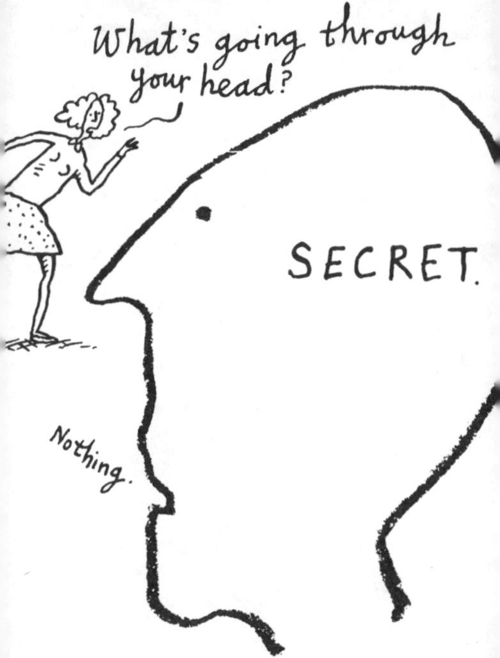
What's going through your head?
SECRET.
Nothing.